IRISH FOLK SONGS

Irish Folk Songs

BILL MEEK

Gill & Macmillan

IN MEMORY OF
JOHN LOGAN WARD,
BALLAD-MAKER
OF KILLENAKIN, CO. DOWN

Gill & Macmillan Ltd
Goldenbridge
Dublin 8
with associated companies throughout the world
© *Selection and Notes, Bill Meek 1997*
0 7171 2533 5
Musical notation by Susan Donohoe
Original text design by Identikit Design Consultants, Dublin
Print origination by Carole Lynch
Printed by ColourBooks Ltd, Dublin

This book is typeset in 10/15 pt Bembo.

A catalogue record is available for this book
from the British Library.

1 3 5 4 2

Contents

Introduction

There was a time in Ireland when the local ballad-maker provided the service of journalist as well as entertainer. By direct oral communication or through the distribution of song sheets, the ballad was an influential medium in spreading the word about the goings-on in the parish, happenings throughout the island as a whole, or indeed news of events in the wide world beyond. Naturally the opinions of the bard tended to colour the reports, and in that respect perhaps not a great deal has changed since newspapers, radio waves, and moving pictures in a box have become a more common currency of communication.

In this collection there are recurrent themes: songs of love, or the lack of it, songs of the famous and songs of the times, of sporting achievement, of humour, and of yearning for the home place. I have not attempted to categorise these formally; often one theme tends to blend into another. The airs (and there are often rival tunes to be found elsewhere) are provided in simple notation but they are not carved in stone, nor indeed are the texts.

The ballad form was developed by way of a gradually changing oral tradition. The present generation has the option and the right to continue this ever evolving process. The songs selected date from the eighteenth into the present century. With a few possible exceptions they are gleaned from the creative reservoir of that most prolific of balladeers commonly known as Anonymous.

First Lines in Alphabetical Order

1. The Banks of the Roses

On the banks of the roses my love and I sat down,
And I took out my violin to play my love a tune,
In the middle of the tune, she sighed and she said
'Arrah, Johnny, lovely Johnny, would you leave me.'

O when I was a young man I heard my father say
That he'd rather see me dead and buried in the clay,
Sooner than be married unto any runaway
By the lovely sweet banks of the roses.

O then I am no runaway and I will let them know,
That I can take a good glass or can leave it all alone,
And the man that doesn't like me he can keep his girl
at home,
And young Johnny will go roving with another.

And if ever I get married 'twill be in the month of May,
When the leaves they are green and the meadows they
are gay,
And I and my true love will sit and sport and play
On the lovely sweet banks of the roses.

*A simple love song, probably from the province of Munster and
sung to a jaunty tune. That said, the words none the less reflect
an era when the ideals of romance and the realities of property
were not entirely unconnected concepts.*

2. The Banks of Claudy

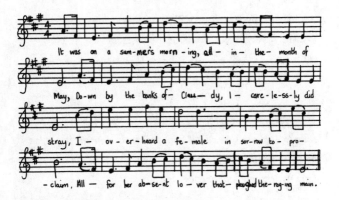

It was on a summer's morning, all in the month of May,
Down by the banks of Claudy, I carelessly did stray,
I overheard a female in sorrow to proclaim,
All for her absent lover that ploughed the raging main.

I stepped up unto her and gave her a surprise;
I own she did not know me, I being in disguise,
Says I 'My fairest creature, my joy and heart's delight,
How far do you mean to wander this dark and dreary
night?'

'It's to the banks of Claudy if you'd be pleased to show,
Take pity on a fair maid who knows not where to go.
I'm searching for a young man and Johnny is his name,
And on the banks of Claudy I'm told he does remain.'

'These are the banks of Claudy, young maid, where on
you stand,
But do not trust your Johnny for he's a false young man,
But do not trust your Johnny for he'll not meet you here,
But tarry with me in the green woods, no danger need
you fear.'

'If Johnny was only here this night he would keep me
from all harm,
But he's on the field of battle, all in his uniform.
He's on the field of battle and his foes he does defy,
Like the royal King of honour all on the walls of Troy.'

'It is six long years or better still since Johnny left
this shore,
A-crossing the main ocean where the thundery
billows roar,
A-crossing the main ocean all in honour and in fame,
But I am told his ship was wrecked near to the coast
of Spain.'

And when she heard this dreadful news she flew in
deep despair,
A-wringing of her hands and a-tearing of her hair,
Saying 'If my Johnny's drownded, no man alive I'll take,
Through lonesome shades and valleys I will wander
for his sake.'

So when he saw her loyalty no longer could he stand,
He flew into her arms saying 'Betsy, I'm your man,'
Saying 'Betsy, I'm your young man and the cause of
all your pain,
But since we've met on Claudy's banks we'll never
part again.'

*This version of a classic theme in balladry is from County Derry
but closely related to songs found further afield, for example, the
Scots 'Bleacher Lassie of Kelvinhaugh'. Later the tune emerged
as that of 'The Singing Bird', much loved among circles
frequenting drawing-room soirées.*

3. The Limerick Rake

I am a young fellow who thinks he is bold,
Near Castletown Conners I'm very well known,
And in Newcastle West I've spent many a note,
With Kitty and Judy and Mary.
My parents reproved me for being such a rake
And for spending my time in such frolicsome ways,
But I ne'er could forget the sweet pleasures of Jane,
Agus fagaimid siúd mar atá sé.

My parents they taught me to shake and to mow,
To plough and to harrow, to reap and to sow,
But my mind was too airy to set it so low,
I set out on a high speculation.
On paper and parchment they learned me to write,
In Euclid and grammar they opened my eyes,
And in multiplication in faith I was bright,
Agus fagaimid siúd mar atá sé.

If I chance for to go to the town of Rathkeale
The girls all around me do flock in the square,
Some buy me a bottle and others sweet cake
To treat me unknown to their parents.
There's one from Askeaton, and one from the Pike,
Another from Arda my heart has beguiled,
But being from the mountains their stockings are white,
And I'd love to be tightening their garters.

If I chance for to go to the market at Croom,
With a cock in my hat and my pipes in full tune,
I'm made welcome at once and brought up to a room
Where Bacchus is sporting with Venus.
There's Peggy and Jane from the town of Bruree,
There's Biddy from Bruff and we all on the spree,
Such a combing of locks there was about me,
Agus fagaimid siúd mar atá sé.

To quarrel for riches I ne'er was inclined,
For the greatest of misers must leave them behind.
I'll buy me a cow that will never run dry
And I'll milk her by twisting her horn.
John Damer of Shrodel had plenty of gold
And Devonshire's treasures a thousand times o'er,
But now he is lying in nettles and mould,
Agus fagaimid siúd mar atá sé.

There's some say I'm foolish but more say I'm wise,
To be fond of the women I know is no crime,
For the son of King David had ten hundred wives,
And his wisdom was highly regarded.
I'll work in my garden and live at my ease,
And each woman and child can partake of the same,
If there's war in the cabin themselves they may blame,
Agus fagaimid siúd mar atá sé.

And now for the future I mean to be wise,
And I'll send for the women who've to me been kind,
And I'll marry them all in the morning bye and bye
If the clergy agree to the bargain.
When I'm on my back and my soul is at peace,
These women will gather and cry by my side,
And all of my children will offer their prayers
To the Lord for the soul of their father.

Gender chauvinist he may have been, but the amorous inclinations of the 'Rake' are in accord with a frequent theme associated with the song-lore of the migrant labourers of the last century.

4. Hand Me Down My Pettycoat

Oh hand me down my pettycoat and hand me
down my shawl,
Hand me down my button boots for I'm off to the
Linenhall.

Chorus
With your he was a quare one, faddle o mo go adat,
He was a quare one, I'll tell you.

If he joined the army all under a false name,
To do me out of the pension sure it's his auld one is all
to blame.
Chorus

Now if you go to the Curragh Camp just ask for
number nine,
You'll see three squaddies standing in a row, and the
one in the middle is mine.
Chorus

Now if you go to the battle line be off and fight the Boer,
We'll try and hold the Dublins back, let the bogmen go
before.
Chorus

My love is o'er the ocean, my love is o'er the sea,
My love he is a darling man, but left me in the family way.
Chorus

*A thoroughly Dublinese, robust and unsentimental comment on
matters pertaining to the heart, dating from a time when
recruitment into the British Army provided an alternative to the
competing discipline of domestic partnership.*

5. Enniskillen Dragoon

A beautiful maiden of fame and renown,

A gentleman's daughter from Monaghan town,

As she rode by the barracks, this beautiful maid

Stood up on her coach to see the Dragoons on parade.

Chorus

Fare you well Enniskillen, I must leave you for a while,

And all thy fair waters round Erin's green isle,

And when the war is over I'll return in full bloom,

And they'll all welcome home their Enniskillen Dragoons.

They were all dressed up the like of gentlemen's sons,
With their fine shining rapiers and their carabine guns,
'O Willie, dearest Willie, you have 'listed full soon
In the third Royal loyal Enniskillen Dragoons.'
Chorus

'Oh Flora, lovely Flora, your pardon I crave,
For now and forever, sure you know I'm your slave,
But your parents they have slighted me morning, night
and noon,
All because it's you love your Enniskillen Dragoon.'
Chorus

'Oh Willie, dearest Willie, heed not what they say,
For children their parents must always obey,
But when you've left Ireland they'll soon change
their tune,
Saying the good Lord be with you, Enniskillen
Dragoon.'
Chorus

*If more romantic than the previous song, this too serves as a
reminder of the days when young Irishmen enlisted in regiments
bound for foreign service, and not always willingly.*

6. Carrickmannon Lake

When out one lovely evening a rambling I did make,
Down by the crystal fountain called Carrickmannon lake,
Down by the crystal fountain an image I did view,
Sure nature never did design an image such as you.

With courage bold undaunted, I boldly then stood forth,
'Oh my delightful charmer, thou Venus of the North,
Give me my way or else I'll stray, my one and only joy,
And sure 'twould be a pity for to kill a harmless boy.'

With flashing eye and ne'er a sigh she boldly turned on me
'Young man depart for in my heart no place I page
for thee,'
And to my further pleading no answer would she make,
But left me there a-standing by Carrickmannon lake.

Killinchy is my dwelling place where first my breath I drew,
Drumrea it is my parents' place — a thousand times adieu,
It's for her sake I'll passage make across the raging sea,
A pilgrim there to do and dare in North Amerikay.

So all young lads a warning take, and shun Killinchy fair,
Likewise sweet Carrickmannon for the cruel one
that's there,
When the sun is slow declining below that hill so clear,
The shadow of her dwelling on the lake it does appear.

*For me this conjures up memories of childhood. When growing
up, 'Killinchy' on the shores of Strangford Lough was indeed 'my
dwelling place'. The house of the lady of the piece is described
with geographic detail in the last verse. I have heard a surname
suggested, but despite the passing of generations I would not
dream of committing this to print.*

7. The Broad Streams of Eochaill

How can I live at the top of a mountain
Without money in my pockets, or gold for to count it?
I would leave the money go — all for to please her fancy,
And I will marry no one but my bonny blue-eyed lassie.

She's my bonny blue-eyed lassie with her glance so sweet
and tender,
Her neck like the swan and her waist so slim and slender,
Her lovely hair in ringlets rare hangs on her snow-white
shoulder,
I will ask her will she marry me — and no man could be
bolder.

Some people say that she's very low in station,
More people say she's the cause of my ruination.
Let them all say what they will — to her I will prove
constant still,
Till the day that I'll die she's my true love, believe me.

Brightly swims the swan on the broad streams of Eochaill,
And loudly sings the nightingale all for to behold her,
On the cold frost and snow the moon it shines deeply —
But deeper by far between me and my true love.

*These lyrical verses were given to me by Seamus Ennis, one of the
greatest influences on traditional music in the twentieth century.
The air is probably of Scots origin. Eochaill is the original name
for the east Cork coastal town of Youghal.*

8. The Orange Maid of Sligo

On Benbulben's high and lofty heights the evening sun
was setting bright,
It cast a ray of golden light around the Bay of Sligo.

A tiny craft with glancing oars and flowing sail the wind
before,
It drove the tiny craft ashore all on the Bay of Sligo.

And looking o'er the vessel's side she saw upon the
waters glide,
An orange lily's golden pride all on the Bay of Sligo.

Make haste, make haste and save the flower that I prize
more than any other,
No traitor must have it in his power around the Bay of
Sligo.

An Orange youth then from the bow did reach the
flower and with a vow
Bestowed it on the lovely brow of the Orange Maid
of Sligo.

She soon became his lovely bride, and oft he thinks at
eventide
About the lily's golden pride all on the Bay of Sligo.

So come all True Blues and fill your glass, a better toast
will never pass,
We'll drink unto that lovely lass, the Orange Maid of
Sligo.

*For all its symbolism, this song from the loyalist tradition has
more to do with romance than affairs of state. Given the political
geography of modern Ireland, it is interesting that the setting is
not the province of Ulster but that of Connaught.*

9. The Flower of Magherally

On a lovely summer's morning
When the flowers all were springing O,
Nature was adorning
And the wee birds sweetly singing O,
I met my love near Banbridge town,
My own and darling Sally O,
And she's the Queen of the County Down,
And the Flower of Magherally O.

With admiration I did gaze,
All on the dark-eyed maiden O,
Adam was never half so pleased
When he first saw Eve in Eden O.
Her skin was like the lily white
That grows in yonder valley O.
And she's my love and my heart's delight,
And the Flower of Magherally O.

An Irish boy although I be,
With neither wealth or treasure O,
Yet I will love my dearest dear,
I will love her beyond measure O.
Had I all the wealth that is possessed
By the great Titherally O,
I'd give't to her that I love the best,
She's the Flower of Magherally O.

Is it coincidence that the 'Flower' happened to come from the same area as the more widely known 'Star of the County Down'? Just one example of many magnificent love songs from that county.

10. The Arrest of Parnell

Come all you gallant Irishmen and listen to my song,
While I a story do relate of England's cruel wrong.
Before this wrong all other wrongs in Ireland do grow
pale,
For they clapped the pride of Erin's isle into cold
Kilmainham Jail.

It was the tyrant Gladstone, and he said unto himself
'I never will be easy till Parnell is on the shelf.
So make a warrant out in haste and take it by the mail,
And we'll clap the pride of Erin's isle in cold Kilmainham
Jail.'

So Buckshot took the warrant and he buttoned up his
coat,
And took the train to Holyhead to catch the Kingstown
boat.
The weather it was rather rough and he was feeling queer,
When Mallon and the polis came to meet him on the pier.

But soundly slept the patriot, for he was killed with work,
Haranguing of the multitudes in Limerick and in Cork,
Till Mallon and the polis came and rung the front-door bell,
Disturbing of his slumbers in bold Morrison's Hotel.

Then up there spoke bold Morrison 'Get up yourself and
run,'
O bright shall shine in history's page the name of Morrison.
'To see the pride of Erin jailed I never could endure;
Slip on your boots, I'll let you out upon the kitchen door.'

But proudly flashed the patriot's eyes as he boldly
answered 'No,
'Twill ne'er be said that Parnell turned his back to face the
foe.
Parnell abú for liberty — sure it's all the same' says he,
'For Mallon has locked the kitchen door and taken away
the key.'

They took him and they bound him, those minions of
the law,
'Twas Pat the Boots was there that night and told me all
he saw.
But ne'er a step the patriot bold would leave the place until
They granted him a ten per cent reduction on the bill.

Had I been there with odds at my back of two hundred
men to one,
It makes my blood run cold to think of the deeds I would
have done,
It isn't here I'd be telling you this melancholy tale,
How they clapped the pride of Erin's isle into cold
Kilmainham Jail.

*Charles Stewart Parnell, the nineteenth-century champion of
Irish Home Rule in the Westminster parliament, was of Anglo-
Irish landed background. However, this ballad, relating his arrest
and imprisonment, was spawned in a less privileged sector of
society.*

11. Johnny I Hardly Knew You

While going on the road to sweet Athy, Huroo, Huroo,

While going on the road to sweet Athy, Huroo, Huroo,

While going on the road to sweet Athy with a stick in my

hand and a drop in my eye

A doleful damsel I heard cry — Johnny I hardly knew you.

Chorus

With your drums and guns and guns and drums,

Huroo, Huroo,

With your drums and guns and guns and drums,

Huroo, Huroo,

With your drums and guns and guns and drums

the enemy nearly slew you,

Oh Johnny dear you look so queer, Johnny I hardly

knew you.

Where are your eyes that looked so mild, Huroo, Huroo,
Where are your eyes that looked so mild, Huroo, Huroo,
Where are the eyes that looked so mild when my heart
you did beguile,
Why did you skedaddle from me and the child, Johnny I
hardly knew you.
Chorus

Where are your arms gone alack, Huroo, Huroo,
Where are your arms gone alack, Huroo, Huroo,
Where are your arms gone alack, I often felt them on
my back,
From pain I roared at every crack, Johnny it's then I
knew you.
Chorus

Where are the legs with which you run, Huroo, Huroo,
Where are the legs with which you run, Huroo, Huroo,
Where are the legs with which you run when off you
went to carry a gun,
Indeed and your dancing days are done, Johnny I hardly
knew you.
Chorus

It grieved my heart to see you sail, Huroo, Huroo,

It grieved my heart to see you sail, Huroo, Huroo,

It grieved my heart to see you sail if my heart you felt you
would bewail,

It shook my head like the tail of a whale, Johnny I hardly
knew you.

Chorus

But still I'm glad to see you home, Huroo, Huroo,

But still I'm glad to see you home, Huroo, Huroo,

But still I'm glad to see you home from the faraway island
of Saloam,

You're so low in flesh and so high in bone, Johnny I hardly
knew you.

Chorus

*The message relayed by this stirring military air relates more to
the futility rather than the glorification of war. The song became
popular in the United States. 'The faraway island of Saloam' is
the country now known as the Republic of Sri Lanka.*

12. My Boy Willie

It was early early all in the spring,
That my boy Willie went to serve the King,
The night was dark and the wind blew high,
It was then I lost my dear sailor boy.

The night is long and I can find no rest,
The thought of Willie it runs in my breast,
And I will search the green woods wide,
Still hoping my true love to find.

'O father, father, give me a boat,
Out on the ocean that I may float,
To watch the big ships as they pass by,
That I might enquire for my sailor boy.'

She was not long out upon the deep,
When a man-o'-war she chanced to meet,
Saying 'Captain, captain, now tell me true,
If my boy Willie is on board with you.'

'What sort of boy is your Willie dear?
And what sort of suit does your Willie wear?'
'He wears a suit of the royal blue,
And you'll easy know him for his heart is true.'

'O then your Willie I am sad to say,
Has just been drownèd the other day,
On yon green island that we pass by,
'Twas there we laid your poor sailor boy.'

She wrung her hands and she tore her hair,
And she sobbed and sighed in her despair,
And with every sob she let fall a tear,
And every sigh it was for Willie dear.

'O father, make my grave both wide and deep,
With a fine tombstone at my head and feet,
And in the middle a turtle dove,
To show the world that I died for love.'

*The image of the young lover drowned at sea is common to the
folk traditions of numerous cultures. This air is shared by one
version of 'The Croppy Boy', a popular patriotic ballad from
Wexford.*

13. The Lambs in the Green Fields

The lambs in the green fields they sport and they play,
And many strawberries grow round the salt sea,
And many strawberries grow round the salt sea,
And many's a ship sails the ocean,
And many's a ship sails the ocean.

The bride and bride's party to the church they do go,
The bride she rides foremost she bears the best show,
And I follow after my heart it is low,
To see my love wed to another,
To see my love wed to another.

The first time I saw them 'twas at the church stand,
With gold on her finger, her love by the hand,
And said I 'My fair lassy, I'll still be your man,
Although you are wed to another,
Although you are wed to another.'

The next time I saw them 'twas on the way home,
And I ran on before them not knowing where to roam,
And said I 'My fair lassy, I'll stand by your side,
Although you are wed to another,
Although you are wed to another.'

'Will you stop' said the groomsman 'Let me have
my word,
If you value your life at the point of my sword,
For courting too slowly you've lost this fair maiden,
Begone for you'll never enjoy her,
Begone for you'll never enjoy her.'

O dig you my grave both long, wide, and deep,
And cover it over with flowers so sweet,
And lay me down in it to take my last sleep,
For that's the best way to forget her,
For that's the best way to forget her.

*Yet another ballad in the classic tradition known to traditional
singers in England, Scotland and North America as well as
Ireland.*

14. The Wild Mountain Thyme

Oh the summertime is coming

And the birds are sweetly singing,

And the wild mountain thyme

All around the blooming heather,

Will you go lassie go?

Chorus

And we'll all go together

To pull wild mountain thyme

All around the blooming heather,

Will you go lassie go?

I will build my love a tower,
By yon pure crystal fountain,
And all around it I will pile
All the flowers of the mountain,
Will you go lassie go?
Chorus

If my true love will not come
Then I'll surely find another
To pull wild mountain thyme
All around the blooming heather,
Will you go lassie go?
Chorus

A love song from the province of Ulster and, like many another from the north-east of Ireland, showing signs of Scottish origin.

15. The Lowlands of Holland

The night that I was married and lay in marriage bed,
Up came the bold sea captain and stood at my bed-head;
Saying 'Arise, arise, young married man and come along
with me
To the Lowlands of Holland to fight the enemy.'

Oh Holland is a wondrous place, and in it grows much green,
It is a place of residence for my love to lie in,
Where the wild flowers grow most plenteously with fruit
on every tree,
But the Lowlands of Holland are between my love and me.

They took my love on board a ship, a ship of noble fame,
With four-and-twenty sailors to steer across the main,
The storms they then began to rise, and the seas began
to shout
And then my love and his gallant ship were sorely tossed
about.

Says the mother to the daughter 'What makes you so
lament?
Is there ne'er a man in Ireland, to please your discontent?'
'Oh there's men enough in Ireland, but none at all for me,
For I only love the one true man and he bides across the
sea.'

'I'll wear no shoe or stocking, or comb put in my hair,
No fire bright nor candlelight shall show my beauty rare.
Nor will I wed with any man until the day I die
Since the Lowlands of Holland are between my love and I.'

*Yet a further example of domestic bliss being interrupted by
foreign wars, in this case with indecent haste.*

16. The Curragh of Kildare

The winter it is past and summer's come at last,
And the birds they sing on every tree,
Their little hearts are glad, but mine is very sad
Since my true love is absent from me.
Repeat last two lines

The rose upon the brier by the water running clear
Gives joy to the linnet and the bee,
Their little hearts are blest, but mine is not at rest,
Since my true love is absent from me.
Repeat last two lines

Fine livery I'll wear and I'll comb down my hair,
And in velvet so green I will appear,
And straight I will repair to the Curragh of Kildare
For it's there I'll get tidings of my dear.
Repeat last two lines

All you that are in love and cannot it remove,

I pity the pains that you endure,

For experience lets me know that your hearts are

full of woe,

It's a woe that no mortal can cure.

Repeat last two lines

*The open expanse of unfenced grazing land in County Kildare
called the Curragh is known as the centre of the Irish equine
industry, and is also the scene for this soliloquy on the pain of
absence.*

17. The Shepherd's Lamb

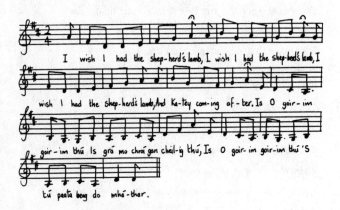

I wish I had the shepherd's lamb,

I wish I had the shepherd's lamb,

I wish I had the shepherd's lamb,

And Katey coming after.

Chorus

Is O goirim goirim thú

Is grá mo chroí gan cheilig thú,

Is O goirim goirim thú,

'S tú peata beag do mháthar.

I wish I had a yellow cow,

I wish I had a yellow cow,

I wish I had a yellow cow,

And welcome from my darling.

Chorus

I wish I had a herd of kine,
I wish I had a herd of kine,
I wish I had a herd of kine,
And Katey from her father.
Chorus

Chorus phonetically
Iss O gwirim gwirim hoo,
Is graw machree gone kellig hoo,
Iss O gwirim gwirim hoo,
Sthoo pathe pyug de wauher.

Chorus translation
And O I hail you, I hail you,
You are the love of my heart without deceit,
And O I hail you, I hail you,
And you are your mother's little pet.

A song about childhood, rather than one gathered from the lore of children. Apart from the odd phrase the items in this collection are in English even if the surrounding ethos is distinctly Irish. The chorus to 'The Shepherd's Lamb' serves as a reminder of the great wealth of song/poetry in the Gaelic language.

18. Mrs McGrath

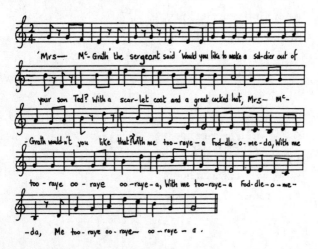

'Mrs McGrath' the sergeant said

'Would you like to make a soldier out of your son Ted?

With a scarlet coat and a great cocked hat,

Mrs McGrath, wouldn't you like that?'

Chorus

With me tooraye-a

Foddle-o-me-da,

With me tooraye ooraye ooraye-a,

With me tooraye-a

Foddle-o-me-da,

Me tooraye ooraye ooraye-a.

Mrs McGrath lived on the sea shore

For the length of seven long years or more,

When a great big ship sailed into the bay

'It's my son Ted with his legs away.'

Chorus

Then up comes Ted without any legs
And in their place two wooden pegs,
She kissed him a dozen times or two
Saying 'My son Ted, is it really you?'
Chorus

'O were you drunk or were you blind
When you left your two fine legs behind?
Or was it walking on the sea
That cut your legs from the knees away?'
Chorus

'I wasn't drunk and I wasn't blind
When I left my two fine legs behind,
But a cannon ball on the fifth of May
Cut my two fine legs from the knees away.'
Chorus

'All foreign war I do proclaim
Between Don John and the King of Spain,
But by jaze I'll make them rue the time
They stole the legs from a son of mine.'
Chorus

A tale of how serving in a foreign conflict could bring tragedy to a family far removed from the battle lines.

19. General Munroe

My name is George Cloakey, at the age of eighteen,
I joined the United Men to fight for the green,
And many's the battle did I then undergo
With our hero commander brave General Munroe.

Have you heard of the Battle of Ballinahinch
When the people oppressed all rose up in defence,
When Munroe left the mountains his men took the field,
Where they fought for twelve hours and they never did
yield.

Munroe being tired and in great want of sleep,
Gave a woman ten guineas his secret to keep.
But when she got the money the devil tempted her so
That she sent for the soldiers and surrendered Munroe.

The soldiers they came and surrounded the place,
They took him to Lisburn and they lodged him in gaol.
His mother and father on passing that way
Heard the very last words that their young son did say.

I die for my country as I fought for her cause,
And I don't fear your soldiers nor yet heed your laws.
So let every true free man who hates Ireland's foe
Fight bravely for freedom like Harry Munroe.

And early next morning when the sun it was low,
They murdered our hero brave General Munroe,
And high oe'r the courthouse stuck his head on a spear,
To make the United Men tremble with fear.

Up rode Munroe's sister, she was dressed all in green,
With a sword in her hand that was well-sharped and keen.
She gave three rousing cheers and away did she go,
Saying 'I'll have revenge for my brother Munroe.'

*During the 1798 Rebellion, Henry Munroe, a Lisburn
shopkeeper of the Presbyterian community, led the United
Irishmen of County Down against the crown forces. This account
is in the words of a small farmer who followed him.*

20. Dunlavin Green

In the year of one thousand seven hundred and ninety-eight,
A sorrowful tale the truth unto you I'll relate,
Of thirty-six heroes to the world were left to be seen,
By a false information were shot down on Dunlavin green.

Bad luck to you, Saunders, for you did their young lives
betray,
You swore a parade would be held there on that very day,
Our drums they did rattle, our fifes they so sweetly did play,
Surrounded we were and privately marched away.

Quite easy they led us as prisoners through the town,
To be slaughtered on the plain, we then were all forced to
lie down,
Such grief and such sorrow were never before there seen,
When the blood ran in streams down the dykes of
Dunlavin green.

There is young Matty Farrell has plenty of cause to complain,
Likewise the two Duffys who were shot down right there
on the plain,
And young Andy Ryan, his mother distracted will run,
For her own brave boy, her belovèd eldest son.

Bad luck to you, Saunders, bad luck may you never shun,
That the widow's curse may melt you like snow in the sun,
The cries of the orphans whose murmurs you never can
screen,
For the murder of all their dear fathers on Dunlavin green.

Some of our boys to the hills they are going away,
Some of them are shot, and some of them going to sea,
Micky Dwyer in the mountains to Saunders has vented
a spleen,
For the murder of his dear companions on Dunlavin green.

*Another incident from 1798, this time from County Wicklow.
Michael Dwyer, mentioned in the last verse, was a United Irish
leader who held out in the mountains long after the rebellion was
crushed. Subsequently he was deported to Australia where,
ironically, he enlisted as a colonial policeman.*

21. The Fenian Man-O'-War

'Twas down by Boston Harbour I carelessly did stray,
I overheard a sailor lad these words to his love say:
'O Bridget, dearest Bridget, from you I must go far
To fight against the cruel foe on the Fenian Man-O'-War.'

'O Patrick, dearest Patrick, don't go away from me,
For the foemen they are treacherous as ever they can be,
And by some cruel dagger you might receive a scar,
O Patrick dear don't venture near the Fenian Man-O'-War.'

They both sat down together, then they arose to stand,
A Fenian crew surrounded him and rowed him from
the land,
Then Patrick raised a Fenian flag and waved it near and far,
And Bridget blessed her sailor boy on board the Man-O'-War.

This reflects how the Separatist movement under the leadership of the Fenian Brotherhood recruited activists not only in Ireland but also in the United States, mostly among veterans of the Civil War. Many Irish sailors achieved distinction in the naval histories of North and South America, as well as several European countries (for example, Barry in the USA, Brown in Argentina, and Wright in Peru and Ecuador). This, however, is possibly the first example of an international maritime adventure in support of Irish republican aspirations. The ship was called The Jackmel, *but renamed* The Erin's Hope.

22. Skibbereen

Oh father dear I oft times heard you talk of Erin's isle,

Her valleys green, her lofty scene, her mountains rude and wild.

You said it was a pleasant place wherein a prince might dwell,

Why have you then forsaken her, the reason to me tell.

My son I loved our native land with energy and pride,

Until a blight came on the land and sheep and cattle died.

The rent and taxes were to pay, I could not them redeem,

And that's the cruel reason why I left old Skibbereen.

It's well I do remember on a black December day,

The landlord and the sheriff came to drive us all away,

They set my roof on fire with their demon yellow spleen,

And that's another reason why I left old Skibbereen.

It's well I do remember in the year of forty-eight,
When we arose with Erin's boys to fight against our fate,
I was hunted through the mountains as an outlaw to the
Queen,
And that's another reason why I left old Skibbereen.

Oh father dear, the day will come when vengeance loud
will call,
And we'll arise with Erin's boys and rally one and all,
I'll be the man to lead the van, beneath our flag of green,
And loud and high we'll raise the cry 'Revenge for
Skibbereen'.

*A conversation between father and son, obviously taking place in
the New World some time after the Young Ireland Rebellion and
in anticipation of the Fenian Rising.*

23. The Orange Lily-O

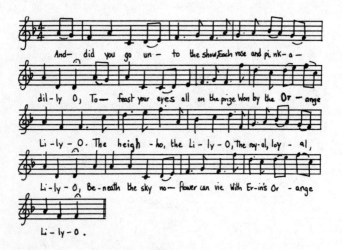

And did you go unto the show,
Each rose and pink-a-dilly-O,
To feast your eyes all on the prize
Won by the Orange Lily-O.

Chorus
The heigh-ho, the Lily-O,
The royal, loyal Lily-O,
Beneath the sky no flower can vie
With Erin's Orange Lily-O.

The Viceroy there so debonair,
Just like a daffydilly-O,
And Lady Clarke, blithe as a lark,
Approached the Orange Lily-O.
Chorus

The ecstatic muse to hear the news
Leapt like a Connacht filly-O,
While gossip fame did loud proclaim
The triumph of the Lily-O.
Chorus

The dandies fine in Bond Street shine,
Gay nymphs in Piccaddily-O,
But fine or gay must yield the day
To Erin's Orange Lily-O.
Chorus

So come brave boys and share her joys,
We'll drink a toast to Willie-O,
Who proudly wore on the Boyne's red shore
The glorious Orange Lily-O.

Final chorus
The heigh-ho, the Lily-O,
The royal, loyal Lily-O.
Fair freedom's flower, may each friendly power
Protect the Orange Lily-O.

*A song from the loyalist camp, yet gentle in sentiment and
untouched by any hint of sectarian rancour.*

24. Daniel O'Connell

Coming home from the fair I met an old woman
With a hump on her back and she blind of an eye,
The day being warm I sat down beside her,
'What news of this man?' the old woman did cry.
'Sure there's no news at all' replied the bold traveller,
'Except that I'm wishing he never had been,
Concerning our hero brave Daniel O'Connell,
Who's now making children in Dublin by steam.'

'O tanam on dia' replied the old woman,
'O children a gra are you crazy at last,
Or it is a sign of a war or rebellion,
O what is the reason they're making so fast.'
'It is not a sign of a war or rebellion,
But that this generation has grown too small —
And they're going to petition the new Lord Lieutenant,
So as not to depend on the old style at all.'

'O there's good men in Ireland as well as in England,
Stout-hearted young fellows by land and by sea,
And if all the young women of Ireland were like them,
O'Connell could throw his steam engine away.
But they are so pugnacious likewise vivacious,
When a young man comes near them they'll spit in his eye,
Which is why they all go as old maids to the corner,
Not a child for to pray for their soul when they die.'

'I am an old woman of three score and ten,
With a hump on my back, ne'er a tooth to be seen,
If the rogue does provoke me I'll lay down a wager,
Sure I'll make better children than him and his steam.
O there's good men in Ireland as well as in England,
Stout-hearted young fellows by land and by sea,
And if all the young women of Ireland were like them,
O'Connell could throw his steam engine away.'

A somewhat light-hearted comment on the reputed private life of
the man regarded by so many of his compatriots as the 'Liberator'.

25. The Western Ocean

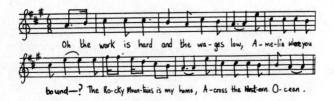

Oh the work is hard and the wages low,
Amelia where you bound?
The Rocky Mountains is my home,
Across the Western Ocean.

It's a land of plenty there you'll find
Amelia where you bound?
I'm off across the Western Sea
To join the Irish Army.

To Liverpool I'll make my way,
Amelia where you bound?
To Liverpool that Yankee school,
Across the Western Ocean.

There's Liverpool Pat with his tarpaulin hat,
Amelia where you bound?
And Yankee John the packet rat,
Across the Western Ocean.

Beware those packet ships, I pray,
Amelia where you bound?
They'll steal your stores and your clothes away,
Across the Western Ocean.

*For an island country, Ireland has comparatively few songs of the
sea, and for this there are many historical and economical
explanations. 'The Western Ocean' is one such in shanty form.
The reference to 'the Irish Army' no doubt related to those
members of the Fenian Brotherhood at that time mobilising in
North America.*

26. The Land of Libertie

My mind it being much inclined to cross the raging main,
I left my tender parents in sorrow, grief and pain.
On board 'The Fame' we then became all passengers to be,
To sail with Captain Thompson to the Land of Libertie.

As we were safely sailing to a place called Newfoundland,
The wind arose ahead of us and our ship was at a stand:
'All hands on deck' bold Thompson cried 'or we'll be cast
away,
All firmly stand or you'll never land in North Amerikay.'

A mount of ice came moving down a-near our gallant main,
But the Lord of Mercy, he was kind our lives for to
maintain.
Our gallant sailors hauled about and so our ship did save,
Or we were doomed to be entombed all in a watery grave.

When we were safely landed our faint hearts we did
renew,
But how could I sleep easy, Erin dear, so far from you.
I hope the time will come again when our comrades all
we'll see,
And once more we'll live together in love and unitie.

*These lines give a realistic account of an aspect of the nineteenth-
century waves of emigration not always remembered, the perils of
an Atlantic sea-crossing in ships often ill-equipped to sustain the
hazards that might arise.*

27. The Kilrane Boys

On the thirteenth day of April in the year of forty-four,

With the bloom of spring the birds did sing around green Erin's shore,

The feathered train in concert their tuneful notes did strain

To resound with acclamation that echoed through Kilrane.

Foul British laws are the whole cause of our going far away;

From the fruits of our hard labour they defraud us here each day.

To see our friends in slavery tied with taxes for to pay.

'Ere we'll be bound to such bloodhounds we'll plough the raging sea.

There's William Whitty and his bride their names I first
will sound,
John Murphy and John Connors from Ballygeary town,
William Lambert and John Donnelly, two youths that
none could stain,
Nicholas Kavanagh and Tom Saunders, four more from
Ballygillane.

From Ballyhire Nick Leary a most superior man,
James Pender, Patrick Howlin, John Murphy from
Hayesland,
Larry Murphy from Kilrane joined them in unity
They're bound for Buenos Aires the land of liberty.

*The well-documented diaspora from Ireland to the United States,
Canada and Australia has overshadowed the fact that there were
those who departed their home country to eventually settle in
South America. In particular they originated in the counties of
Westmeath and Wexford, the home of the Kilrane Boys. In
1987 I had the pleasure of enjoying the hospitality of one of the
Kilrane descendants while on a visit to Argentina to make a series
of documentary radio programmes on the Irish community. There
would appear to be an identifiable author to this ballad, a local
schoolmaster by the name of Walter McCormack or Cormack.*

28. The Holy Ground

Farewell to you my darling, a thousand times adieu,

Our good ship soon is sailing to take me far from you,

To leave my fair Diana, she's the girl I do adore,

And still I live in hopes to see the Holy Ground once more.

Chorus

Fine girl you are (*roared*) You're the girl I do adore,

And still I live in hopes to see the Holy Ground once

more — Fine girl you are.

And now we're salt sea sailing and you are far behind,
Kind letters I will write you with the secrets of my mind,
The secrets of my mind, you're the girl I do adore,
And still I live in hopes to see the Holy Ground once more.
Chorus

I see a storm approaching, I see it coming soon,
The night is dark and dreary and I cannot see the moon,
And our good ship is all tossing about and the rigging is all
tore,
And still I live in hopes to see the Holy Ground once more.
Chorus

And now the storm is all over, and we are safe ashore,
We'll drink a toast to the Holy Ground and the girls we
do adore,
We'll drink strong ale and porter till we make the tap
room roar,
And when our money is all spent we'll go to sea and make
some more.
Chorus

*A rousing pint-swilling chorus in praise of Cobh, the deep sea
port serving the city of Cork. It is of course possible that some of
the maritime enthusiasts of the south coast might dispute the
claim that the song in all probability is based on similar verses
celebrating 'Swansea Town'. Such is the folk process!*

29. The Famine Song

Oh the praties they are small over here,

Oh the praties they are small over here,

Oh the praties they are small and way up in Donegal

We eat them skins and all over here, over here,

We eat them skins and all over here.

Oh I wish that we were geese night and morn,

Oh I wish that we were geese night and morn,

Oh I wish that we were geese till the hour of our release,

When we'd live and die in peace stuffing corn,

stuffing corn,

When we'd live and die in peace stuffing corn.

Oh they'll grind us into dust over here,

Oh they'll grind us into dust over here,

Oh they'll grind us into dust, but the Lord in whom
we trust,

Will repay us crumb for crust over here, over here,

Will repay us crumb for crust over here.

*Some songs previously quoted are a reminder that it was the sea
which opened up the escape route for the thousands who fled the
dreadful conditions arising from the Famine in the 1840s.
However, for many it was an escape from one form of inevitable
death to another. The imagery of this song, of which there are
many versions, suggests that it was constructed in sympathetic
comment on the plight of famine victims rather than as a result of
personal experience.*

30. The Rocks of Baun

Come all you loyal heroes wherever you may be,

Don't sign up for any master till you know what your
work may be,

Don't sign up for any master from the clear daylight till the
dawn,

For he only will expect you to plough the Rocks of Baun.

My clothes they are well worn and the rain comes
tumbling in,

My old brogues they are battered now, and I'm feared that
I might give in,

But I'll rise up in the morning from the clear daylight till
the dawn,

And I know I'll never be able to plough the Rocks of
Baun.

My curse attend you, Sweeney, for you have me nearly robbed,
Your sitting by your fireside with your dudeen in your gob,
Your sitting by your fireside from the clear daylight to the dawn,
And you know you'll never be able to plough the Rocks of Baun.

So rise up, lovely Sweeney, and give your horse some hay,
And give to it some oats to eat before you start the day.
Don't feed it on raw turnip, boy, take it down to my green lawn,
And then you'll maybe be able to plough the Rocks of Baun.

O I wish the Queen of England would write to me in time,
And place me in some regiment all in my youth and prime,
I'd fight for Ireland's glory from the clear daylight to the dawn,
And never would return again to plough the Rocks of Baun.

One example taken from the song-lore of the spalpeens, the wandering labourers from poor agricultural land who sought seasonal, and usually ill-paid, employment from 'strong' farmers. The dudeen mentioned in the third verse is a clay pipe.

31. The Boys of Mullaghbawn

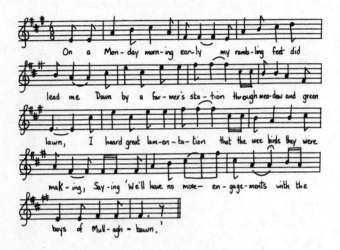

On a Monday morning early my rambling feet did lead me
Down by a farmer's station through meadow and green
lawn,
I heard great lamentation that the wee birds they were
making,
Saying 'We'll have no more engagements with the boys
of Mullaghbawn.'

Squire Jackson is unequalled for honour and for reason,
He never turned a traitor or betrayed the rights of man.
But now we are in danger from a vile deceiving stranger,
Who has ordered transportation for the boys of
Mullaghbawn.

As those heroes crossed the ocean I'm told the boat
in motion
Did stop in wild commotion, as if the seas ran dry,
The trout and salmon gaping while the cuckoo left
its station
Saying 'Farewell to lovely Erin and the hills of
Mullaghbawn.'

To end my lamentation we are in consternation,
And for lack of education I here must end my song.
None seeks for recreation for without consideration
We're sent in transportation from the hills of
Mullaghbawn.

*A transportation lament from south Armagh. The 'heroes' of
Mullaghbawn were probably compelled to leave their country for
engaging in Combination, an early form of agricultural trade
unionism.*

32. Donnelly and Cooper

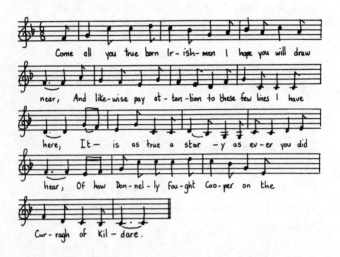

Come all you true born Irishmen I hope you will draw near,

And likewise pay attention to these few lines I have here,

It is as true a story as ever you did hear,

Of how Donnelly fought Cooper on the Curragh of Kildare.

It was on the third of June, my boys, the challenge was sent o'er,

From Britannia to old Grania for to raise her son once more,

To renew the satisfaction and the credit to record,

They are all in deep distraction since brave Daniel conquered all.

Old Grania read the challenge and received it with a smile,
'You'd better haste unto Kildare my well-belovèd child,
It is there you'll reign victorious as you often did before,
And your deeds will shine most glorious around sweet
Erin's shore.'

The challenge was accepted and those heroes did prepare,
To meet brave Captain Kelly on the Curragh of Kildare,
Those Englishmen bet ten to one that day against brave
Dan,
Such odds as that could n'er dismay the blood of an
Irishman.

When those two bully champions were stripped off in
the ring,
They then were full determined each other's blood to spill,
From six to nine they parried till Donnelly knocked him
down,
And Grania smiled 'Well done my child, that is ten
thousand pounds.'

The second round that Cooper fought he knocked down
Donnelly,
And Dan likewise being of true game he rose most
furiously,
Right active then was Cooper, he knocked Donnelly
down again,
Those Englishmen they gave three cheers saying 'The
battle is all in vain.'

Long life to brave Miss Kelly, 'tis recorded on the plain,
She boldly stepped into the ring saying 'Dan, what do you
mean?
Well done' says she 'brave Donnelly, my Irish boy' says she
'My whole estate I have laid out on you, brave Donnelly.'

Then Donnelly rose up again and meeting with great
might,
For to stagnate those nobles all, he continued on to fight.
Though Cooper stood in his own defence exertion
proved in vain,
For he soon received a temple blow which hurled him o'er
the rails.

You sons of proud Britannia, your boasting now recall,
Since Cooper by Dan Donnelly has met a sad downfall,
In eleven rounds he got nine knock-downs likewise a
broken jawbone,
'Shake hands' said she 'brave Donnelly, the battle is all
our own.'

*The year, that of the battle of Waterloo; the venue, the
aforementioned Curragh of Kildare; the event, a pugilistic
encounter fought long before the tempering discipline of the
Queensbury Rules. Dan Donnelly had exceedingly long arms,
one of which is to this day on view in mummified form in a
hostelry in the town of Kilcullen.*

33. The Old Leather Breeches

At the sign of 'The Bell', near the town of Clon-mel, Pat Heg-ar-ty kept a neat ca-bin, Sold pig's meat and bread, Kept a good lodg-ing bed, And was liked in the coun-try he lived in. Now he and his wife they trav-elled through life, On week-days he mend-ed the ditch-es; But on Sun-days he dressed in a suit of the best And his pride was his old leath-er bree-ches.

At the sign of 'The Bell', near the town of Clonmel,
Pat Hegarty kept a neat cabin,
Sold pig's meat and bread, kept a good lodging bed,
And was liked in the country he lived in.
Now he and his wife they travelled through life,
On weekdays he mended the ditches;
But on Sundays he dressed in a suit of the best
And his pride was his old leather breeches.

Now last winter's snow left Patrick so low,

That he was all ate up completely,

With the snow coming down he could not get to town

And hungry guests bothered him greatly.

Then one freezing night like a plague and a blight

Came travellers round Patrick like leeches,

And they swore by the dog if they didn't get prog

They'd eat him clean out of his breeches.

So Pat in his dread went up to his bed

Where Judy his darling wife lay in,

And the two there agreed they'd all have a feed,

So he went and he brought a big knife in.

He cut off the waist of his breeches, the baste,

And he sliced them up buttons and stitches,

Then he carved them in stripes the way you'd cut tripes,

And he boiled them, his old leather breeches.

See how they smiled when they thought he had boiled,

Some mutton or beef of the richest.

'Twas little they knew it was leather burgoo,

Made out of the seat of his breeches.

Round the mess and the stuff said gruff Darby

'It's tough,'

Said Mickeen 'You're no judge of mutton,'

When Brian O'Rourke at the end of his fork

Held up a big ivory button.

*Said Mickeen 'What's that? I thought it was fat,'
Brian leaps to his feet and he screeches:
'By the powers above I was trying to shove
My teeth through the flap of his breeches.'*
They all rushed at Pat but he cut out of that
For he ran when he saw them all rising,
Cried Brian 'Make haste, will you send for the priest,
By the holy Saint Patrick I'm poisoned.'

Reprise ✶ *to* ✶
Revenge for the joke they had for they broke,
All the tables and chairs and the dishes,
And from that very night they'd cut out your sight
At the mention of old leather breeches.

A humorous saga not dissimilar to the sort of nonsense thoroughly enjoyed on the vaudeville circuits, and yet somehow escaping the embarrassment of stage paddy-whackery.

34. The Galbally Farmer

One evening of late as I happened to stray,

To the County Tipperary I was making my way,

To dig the potatoes and work by the day —

I hired with a Galbally farmer.

I asked him how far we were bound for to go,

The night it was dark and the north wind did blow,

I was hungry and tired and my spirits were low

For I got neither whiskey nor porter.

This niggardly miser he mounted his steed,

To the Galbally mountains he posted with speed,

And surely I thought that my poor heart would bleed

To be trudging behind that ould naygur.

When we came to his house sure I entered it first,

It seemed like a kennel or ruined old church,

Says I to myself 'I am left in the lurch

In the house of old Darby O'Leary.'

I well recollect it was Michaelmas night,
To a hearty good supper he did me invite,
A cup of sour milk that would physic a snipe,
'Twould give you the trotting disorders.
The wet old potatoes would poison the cats,
The barn where my bed was 'twas swarming with rats,
It's little I thought it would e'er be my lot
To lie in that hole until morning.

And by what he had said to me I had understood
That my bed in the barn it was not very good,
The blanket was made at the time of the Flood,
The quilt and the sheets in proportion.
'Twas on this old miser I looked with a frown,
When he brought out the straw for to make my shake-down,
I wished that I'd never seen Galbally town,
Or the sky over Darby O'Leary.

I've worked in Kilconnell, I've worked in Kilmore,
I've worked in Knockrainey and Shanballymore,
In Pallas-a-Nicker and Sollohodmore
With decent respectable farmers.
I've worked in Tipperary, the Rag and Rosgreen,
At the mount of Kilfeakle, the bridge of Aleen,
But such woeful starvation I never yet seen
As I got from ole Darby O'Leary.

*Another song from the spalpeen tradition, albeit expressed in a
spirit of witty defiance. Hiring fairs, at which the stock on display
for barter was of the human species, were a regular social and
economic occurrence in the 1800s. In fact they did not totally
disappear until the mid twentieth century.*

35. The Granemore Hare

On last Sat-ur-day mor-ning our horns they did blow, To the
green fields round Tos-sagh our hunts-men did go, For to meet the bold
sports-men from round Kea-dy town, No me love the sport bet-ter than the
boys of May-down.

On last Saturday morning our horns they did blow,
To the green hills round Tassagh our huntsmen did go,
For to meet the bold sportsmen from round Keady town,
None love the sport better than the boys of Maydown.

And when we arrived they were all standing there,
So we took to the green fields in search of a hare,
We did not go far when someone gave a cheer,
Over high hills and valleys this puss she did steer.

When she got to the heather she tried them to shun,
But our dogs never missed one inch where she run,
And they all kept well packed when going over the hill,
For they set for themselves that this puss they would kill.

With our dogs all abreast and that big mountain hare,
And the sweet charming music that rang through the air,
Straight for the Black Bank for to try them once more,
And it was her last sight round the hills of Granemore.

And as they trailed on to where puss she did lie,
She sprang to her feet for to bid them goodbye,
Their music it ceased and her cry we could hear,
Saying 'Bad luck to the ones brought you Maydown
dogs here.'

'Last night as I lay content in the glen,
'Twas little I thought of dogs or of men,
But when going home at the clear break of day,
I could hear the long horn that young Toner does play.'

'It being so early I stopped for a while,
It was little I thought they were going to meet Coyle.
If I had known that I'd have lain near the town,
And tried to get clear of those dogs from Maydown.'

'And now that I'm dying the sport is all done,
No more round the green fields of Keady I'll run,
Or feed in the glen on a long winter's night,
Nor go home to my den when it's breaking daylight.'

'I blame Owen McMahon for bringing Coyle here,
He's been at this auld caper for many's a year,
Every Saturday and Sunday he'll ne'er give it o'er,
With a pack of strange dogs round the hills of Granemore.'

*The opening verses would seem to be in celebration of the exploits
of a pack of south Ulster beagles, and yet ultimately the sympathy
of the bard is entirely with the dying hare.*

36. The Boston Burglar

I was born in Boston city, boys,
It's a place you all know well,
Brought up by honest parents
And the truth to you I'll tell.
Brought up by honest parents
And raised most tenderly,
Till I became a sporting blade
At the age of twenty-three.

My character was taken
And I was sent to jail,
My parents tried to bail me out
But their efforts were in vain.
The jury found me guilty
And the clerk he wrote it down,
The judge he passed my sentence
And I was sent to Charlestown.

I can see my aged father
A-standing by the bar,
I can see my aged mother too
A-pulling her grey hair.
A-pulling at her old grey locks
As the tears came tumbling down,
Saying 'John my son, what have you done
To be sent to Charlestown?'

There's a girl in Boston city, boys,
A place you all know well,
And if I had my liberty
It's with her I would dwell.
If only I had my liberty
Bad company I would shun,
The robbing of the Munster bank
And the drinking of the rum.

You lads that have your liberty,
Protect it while you can.
Don't roam the streets by day or night
Or break the laws of man.
For if you do you'll come to ruin
And you'll end up like me
A-serving up your twenty-one years
In the Royal Artillery.

A young man's account of his descent into a life of crime, with
references to places or events on both sides of the Atlantic.

37. Whiskey in the Jar

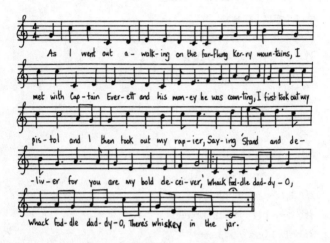

As I went out a-walking on the far-flung Kerry mountains,
I met with Captain Everett and his money he was counting,
I first took out my pistol and I then took out my rapier,
Saying 'Stand and deliver, for you are my bold deceiver.'

Chorus
Whack faddle daddy-O,
Whack faddle daddy-O,
There's whiskey in the jar. (*Repeat*)

I counted out his money and it made a pretty penny,
I'll take it off and give it to my bonny, sporting Jenny.
She sighed and she swore and she said she'd ne'er betray me,
But the devil take the women for they never can be easy.
Chorus

I went up to my chamber all for to take a slumber,
I dreamt of gold and jewels, and sure it was no wonder,
For Jenny drew my charges and she filled them up with
water,
And sent for Captain Everett to be ready for the slaughter.
Chorus

It was early in the morning between six o'clock and seven,
Up rode a band of footmen and likewise Captain Everett,
I first produced my pistol for she'd stolen away my rapier,
But I couldn't shoot the water so a prisoner I was taken.
Chorus

There's only one to help me now, 'tis my brother in the army,
But I don't know where he's stationed, be it Cork or in
Killarney.
But if he comes to free me we'll go wandering in Kilkenny,
I'll engage he'll treat me better than my darling, sporting
Jenny.
Chorus

*One of a number of ballads arising out of the lifestyle of the Irish
highwayman. Other examples are more explicit as to the identity
of the outlaw concerned, e.g. 'Brennan on the Moor', 'Bold
Captain Freney', 'Valentine O'Hara', 'Willie Crotty' and
'Redmond O'Hanlon'.*

38. Rosin the Bow

I've travelled this wide world over,

But now to another I go,

And I know that good quarters are waiting

To welcome old Rosin the Bow,

To welcome old Rosin the Bow,

To welcome old Rosin the Bow,

I know that good quarters are waiting

To welcome old Rosin the Bow.

When I'm dead and laid out on the counter

A voice you will hear from below,

Saying 'Bring out a barrel of porter

To drink to old Rosin the Bow,'

To drink to old Rosin the Bow,

To drink to old Rosin the Bow,

Saying 'Bring out a barrel of porter

To drink to old Rosin the Bow.'

I see Sergeant Death is approaching,
A fierce and a terrible foe.
But I'll raise up my glass to his honour,
Come and drink with old Rosin the Bow,
Come and drink with old Rosin the Bow,
Come and drink with old Rosin the Bow,
But I'll raise up my glass to his honour,
Come and drink with old Rosin the Bow.

*A moment of gentle sentimentality and nostalgia — an old
fiddler contemplates the impending hereafter with a fair degree
of quiet confidence.*

39. The Cruise of the Calibar

Come all you dry land sailors
And listen to my song,
There's only forty verses
So I'll not detain you long,
Concerning the adventures
Of this old Lisburn tar,
Who sailed as a man before the mast
On board of the Calibar.

The Calibar was a spanking craft
Copper-bottomed fore and aft,
Her helm it stuck far out behind
And her wheel was a great big shaft.
With half a gale to fill her sail
She could make one knot per hour.
She's the fastest craft on the Lagan Canal
And she's only the one horse power.

Now the skipper he up and says to me
'Look here my boy' says he:
'Would you like to be a sailor
And sail the mighty sea?
Would you like to be a sailor
The foreign seas to roll?
For we're under orders for Portadown
With a half a ton of coal.'

And in the morning we set sail
The weather it was sublime.
When passing under the old Queen's Bridge
You could hear the Albert chime.
Until we came to the Gasworks Straits,
A very dangerous part,
Where we ran on to a lump of coal
That wasn't put down on the chart.

Then all became confusion
And loud the winds did blow,
And bosun slipped on an orange peel
And fell into the hold below.
'Put up more steam,' the Captain cried,
'For we are sorely pressed.'
But the engineer on the bank replied
'Sure the old horse is doing his best.'

We fell into the water
And let out a terrible roar,
A farmer was standing there on the bank and he threw in the end
of his galluses (spoken)
And he hauled us all ashore,
So I've done with salt-sea sailing
All on the raging main.
And the next time I'm bound for Portadown
By God and I'm going by train.

A valiant tale of reckless maritime adventure. Depending on the
local loyalty of the singer, the Calibar is reported to have cruised
on different inland waterways, including the Grand Canal. This
particular epic voyage took place on the Lagan Canal.

40. The Parting Glass

Of all the money that e'er I had,

I spent it in good company,

And of all the harm I ever have done,

Alas I did it to none but me.

And all I have said through lack of wit

To memory now I can't recall.

Come fill to me the parting glass,

Good luck and joy be with you all.

Of all the comrades I e'er did have

They're sorry at my going away,

And of all the sweethearts I e'er did have,

They wished I'd stay another day.

But since it falls unto my lot,

That I must go and you must not,

I'll gently rise and softly call,

Goodnight and joy be with you all.

If I had money enough to spend,
And leisure time to sit awhile,
There is a fair maid in this town,
And I own she has my heart beguiled.
Her rosy cheeks and ruby lips,
I know she has my heart enthralled,
So fill to me the parting glass,
Goodnight and joy be with you all.

Verses sharing the same melody as other songs of farewell such as
'The American Wake'. They provide a suitable ending to a night
of music, also indeed to this little collection of songs.